They need somebody, maybe you,
to **help them** bake a batch or two.

Help them choose a recipe.
All puffins just love muffins!

All Puffins Just Love Muffins

by Jane Quinn
illustrated by Bill Dare

SCHOLASTIC INC.

New York • Toronto • London • Auckland • Sydney
Mexico City • New Delhi • Hong Kong • Buenos Aires

Designed by Maria Lilja
ISBN-13 978-0-545-01662-9 • ISBN-10: 0-545-01662-2
Copyright © 2008 by Scholastic Inc.
All rights reserved. Printed in China.

First printing, January 2008

12 11 10 9 8 7 6 5 4 3   11 12 13/0

Just look at **all** the hungry puffins —
dreaming **all** day long of muffins.

2

Help them measure carefully.
All puffins **just** love muffins!

Help them add the eggs — **just** a few.
All puffins **just** love muffins!

Help them add the flour, too.
All puffins just love muffins!

Help them mix the berries in.
All puffins **just** love muffins!

Help them fill each muffin tin.
All puffins just love muffins!

Just one more thing for **them** to do —

all by themselves, no **help** from you. . .

Time for **them** to EAT THE MUFFINS!
And, as you can tell,
all the puffins do this well.

Because...
all puffins **just** love muffins!

Sight Word Review

Do you know the four sight words in this book? Read aloud the word on each muffin.

them

just

help

all

help

all

them

just

14

Sight Word Fill-ins

Listen to the sentences. Then choose a sight word from the box to fill in each blank.

Word Box   help   them   all   just

1 I can _____ you tie your shoes.

2 She _____ loves that movie!

3 Where did you put _____?

4 We gave _____ of the puppies away.

5 He likes to _____ his mom rake leaves.

6 I had _____ one cookie.

7 Their teacher took _____ to the museum.

8 Where did _____ of the ducks go?

Sight Word Cheers

Celebrate the new sight words you learned by saying these four short cheers.

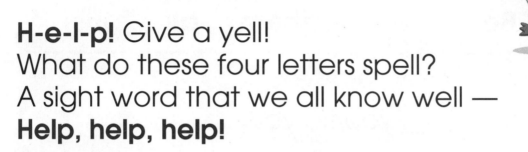

H-e-l-p! Give a yell!
What do these four letters spell?
A sight word that we all know well —
Help, help, help!

T-h-e-m! Give a yell!
What do these four letters spell?
A sight word that we all know well —
Them, them, them!

A-l-l! Give a yell!
What do these three letters spell?
A sight word that we all know well —
All, all, all!

J-u-s-t! Give a yell!
What do these four letters spell?
A sight word that we all know well —
Just, just, just!